PEOPLE IN YOUR
NEIGHBORHOOD

Featuring Jim Henson's Sesame Street Muppets

by Jeffrey Moss
illustrated by Richard Brown

Based on the song, "PEOPLE IN YOUR NEIGHBORHOOD"
© Festival Attractions, Inc. 1969, music and lyrics by Jeffrey Moss

This educational book was created in cooperation with the Children's
Television Workshop, producers of Sesame Street. Children do not have
to watch the television show to benefit from this book. Workshop
revenues from this product will be used to help support CTW
educational projects.

A SESAME STREET/GOLDEN PRESS BOOK

Published by Western Publishing Company, Inc. in conjunction with Children's Television Workshop.

Who are the people in your neighborhood,
The people that you meet each day?

The MAIL CARRIER always brings the mail
Through rain or snow or sleet or hail.
He'll work and work the whole day through
To get your letters safe to you.

The BAKER is the one who makes
Your bread and rolls and pies and cakes.
If you want something sweet to eat, go see
The BAKER in the bakery.

The NEWS DEALER'S the one you need
If you want to get something to read.
Want a paper or a paperback book?
The newsstand is the place to look.

The CLEANER is the one who knows
How to clean and press your finest clothes.
He'll take a jacket, suit, or vest
And clean it so you'll look your best.

A TEACHER works the whole day through
To teach important things to you.
He'll teach you things you won't forget
Like numbers and the alphabet.

A BARBER has a great big chair.
You sit in it, he cuts your hair.
He'll snip and clip and never rest
Until your haircut looks its best.

The Bus Driver drives fast or slow
To take you where you want to go.
When you get in and pay your fare
She will drive you anywhere.

A DENTIST cares for all your teeth,
The top ones and the ones beneath.
So if you have an aching tooth,
He'll fix it quick, and that's the truth.

FIREFIGHTERS are brave, it's said.
Their engine is a shiny red.
If there's a fire anywhere about
They'll be sure to put it out.

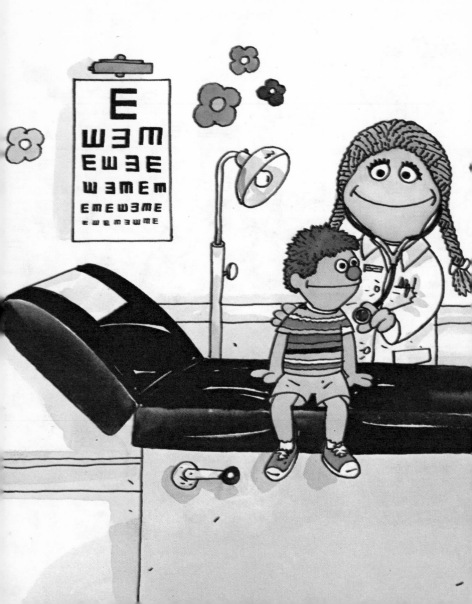

The DOCTOR makes you well real quick
If by chance you're feeling sick.
She works and works the whole day long
To help you feel well and strong.

The TRASH COLLECTOR works hard each day.
He'll always take your trash away.
He drives the biggest truck you've ever seen
To keep the city streets all clean.

The SHOEMAKER is always there
To take care of the shoes you wear.
With his hammer, nails, and glue
He'll fix your shoes as good as new.

The GROCER sells the things you eat
Like bread and eggs and cheese and meat.
No matter what you're looking for,
You'll find it at the grocery store.

Who are the people in your neighborhood?
They're the people that you meet
When you're walking down the street.
They're the people that you meet each day!